Moon Patterns

Description

Learners explore the phenomenon that the Moon's appearance changes through-out a month. After reading a fiction book that depicts the Moon phases, they study Moon calendars and describe the shapes and pattern they observe. After reading a nonfiction book and creating a tool to remember the pattern, they predict the next phases on a Moon calendar.

Alignment With the *Next Generation Science Standards*

Performance Expectation		
1-ESS1-1: Use observations of the Sun, Moon, and stars to describe patterns that can be predicted.		
Science and Engineering Practices	**Disciplinary Core Idea**	**Crosscutting Concepts**
Asking Questions and Defining Problems Ask questions based on observations to find more information about the natural and/or designed worlds. Analyzing and Interpreting Data Use observations (firsthand or from media) to describe patterns in the natural world in order to answer scientific questions. Obtaining, Evaluating, and Communicating Information Read grade-appropriate texts and/or use media to obtain scientific and/or technical information to determine patterns in and/or evidence about the natural and designed world(s).	ESS1.A: The Universe and Its Stars Patterns of the motion of the Sun, Moon, and stars in the sky can be observed, described, and predicted.	Patterns Patterns in the natural world can be observed, used to describe phenomena, and used as evidence. Stability and Change Some things stay the same while other things change. Things may change slowly or rapidly.

Note: The activities in this lesson will help students move toward the performance expectations listed, which is the goal after multiple activities. However, the activities will not by themselves be sufficient to reach the performance expectations.

Featured Picture Books

TITLE: **A Moon of My Own**
AUTHOR: **Jennifer Rustgi**
ILLUSTRATOR: **Ashley White**
PUBLISHER: **Dawn Publications**
YEAR: **2016**
GENRE: **Story**
SUMMARY: *A young girl travels the world in a dream with her faithful companion the Moon, showing Moon phases from iconic places on all seven continents.*

TITLE: **Next Time You See the Moon**
AUTHOR: **Emily Morgan**
PHOTOGRAPHS BY: **Tom Uhlman, Steven David Johnson, Judd Patterson, and NASA**
PUBLISHER: **NSTA Kids**
YEAR: **2014**
GENRE: **Non-Narrative Information**
SUMMARY: *Simple explanations and photographs show how the Moon phases occur in a predictable pattern and are caused by the Moon's orbit around Earth.*

Time Needed

This lesson will take several class periods. Suggested scheduling is as follows:

Session 1: Engage with A Moon of My Own Read-Aloud

Session 2: Explore with Moon Calendar

Session 3: Explain with Next Time You See the Moon Read-Aloud

Session 4: Elaborate with Moon Wheel and What Comes Next?

Session 5: Evaluate with A Moon of My Own Silhouette Paintings and Moon Patterns

Materials

For Moon Calendar:

- January Moon Calendar to project (or download the current month; see StarDate's Moon Phase Calculator in "Websites" section)

For Moon Wheel (per student):

- Moon Wheel pages copied on cardstock
- Brass brad

For A Moon of My Own Silhouette Paintings (per student):

- Black construction paper (two sheets)

- Paintbrush
- White poster paint
- 5 shades of blue poster paint (light to dark)

For What Comes Next?

- February Moon Calendar to project (or download next month's; see StarDate's Moon Phase Calculator in the "Websites" section)

Student Pages

- January Moon Calendar (or download and print the current month; see StarDate's Moon Phase Calculator in the "Websites" section)
- Moon Wheel 1 and 2
- Moon Patterns (½ page, cut out)
- STEM Everywhere

Background for Teachers

From the time they are very young, children are naturally curious about the Moon. Some planets have many moons, but the Moon we see is Earth's only natural satellite. It is about one-fourth the size of Earth and is made of rock. There is no air on the Moon and no signs of life (though evidence of frozen water has recently been discovered). The Moon reflects the Sun's light; it has no light of its own. It takes 27.3 days for the Moon to revolve around, or orbit, Earth. It takes that same amount of time to rotate, or spin, on its axis. This causes the same side of the Moon to be facing Earth at all times. The side of the Moon facing away from Earth has been photographed only from spacecraft.

Half of the Moon is always illuminated by the Sun and half is dark, but the shape of the Moon appears to change throughout the month when viewed from Earth. The stages in this predictable, repeating cycle are known as Moon phases. These phases occur because you see different parts of the lighted side of the Moon from Earth at different times during its orbit. When the Moon is almost directly between the Sun and Earth, you can't see any of the lighted side. This is called a new Moon. In a few days, you start to see a tiny sliver of the lighted side, a crescent Moon. When the Moon is a quarter of its way around Earth, you see half of the lighted half, or a quarter Moon. When you can observe almost the whole lighted half, it is called a gibbous Moon. Next, you see the whole lighted half, or a full Moon. After a full Moon, you see less of the lighted half, another gibbous Moon. Then you see half of the lighted half, another quarter Moon. Next, you see a tiny sliver of the lighted side, another crescent Moon. Finally, you can't see any of the lighted half, and it's the new Moon phase again. As you begin to see more and more of the lighted side of the Moon, it is said to be waxing. When the right side of the Moon looks bright, then the Moon is in its waxing phase. "Light on the right, the Moon is getting bright." (This only applies when viewing the Moon in the Northern Hemisphere.) After a full Moon, you start to see less and less of the lighted side, so the Moon is said to be waning.

The Framework for K–12 Science Education suggests that students in grades K–2 recognize that the patterns of the motion of the Sun, Moon, and stars in the sky can be observed, described, and predicted. In this lesson, students observe the Moon phases, recognize that they occur in a pattern, and predict the next phase based on that pattern. The lesson does not focus on the reason for the Moon phases. Although the nonfiction book shared does mention the reason for the phases, students are not

held accountable for that understanding as this point. Observing, describing, and predicting the phases lays the foundation for understanding the reason for the Moon phases in later grades. The crosscutting concept (CCC) of patterns is integral to this lesson as students observe, describe, and predict the Moon phases, as is the CCC of stability and change. The science and engineering practice (SEP) of asking questions and defining problems is used as students study Moon calendars and record what they notice and what they are wondering. The SEP of analyzing and interpreting data is used as students share their observations of the Moon, describe patterns, and make predictions. And the SEP of obtaining, evaluating, and communicating information is used as students use text and media to look for patterns, explanations, and terminology.

Learning Progressions

Below are the disciplinary core idea (DCI) grade band endpoints for grades K–2 and 3–5. These are provided to show how student understanding of the DCI in this lesson will progress in future grade levels.

DCI	Grades K–2	Grades 3–5
ESS1.A: The Universe and Its Stars	• Patterns of the motion of the Sun, Moon, and stars in the sky can be observed, described, and predicted.	• The Sun is a star that appears larger and brighter than other stars because it is closer. Stars range greatly in their distance from Earth.

Source: Willard, T., ed. (2015). The NSTA quick-reference guide to the NGSS: Elementary school. Arlington, VA: NSTA Press.

engage

A Moon of My Own Read-Aloud

Connecting to the Common Core
Reading: Literature
INTEGRATION OF KNOWLEDGE AND IDEAS: 1.7

Making Connections: Text to Self

Show students the cover of A Moon of My Own and introduce the author and illustrator. If you like, set the mood for this dreamlike book by turning down the lights and playing some calming music or night sounds. Read the book aloud, or have an astronaut on the International Space Station read it! A Moon of My Own is a featured book on Story Time From Space (see the "Websites" section).

After reading, ask

? Have you ever felt like the Moon was following you?

? What do you notice about the illustrations?

? The illustrations look like nighttime, but have you ever seen the Moon during the day?

? Do you recognize any of the places in the book?

Allow students time to share as you flip through the illustrations, and then show pages 28–29 where each place is identified and represented on a world map. Then ask

? Is it possible to see the Moon in all of these places? (yes)

? What do you notice about the shape of the Moon in the illustrations? (The shape changes. Note: At this point, don't worry about intro-

ducing the names of the phases; that will come later.)

? Have you seen the Moon lately? What did it look like? What time of day or night was it? (Answers will vary.)

Encourage students to observe the Moon over the next few days and notice its shape. You may also want to take students outside to observe the Moon during the school day. You can find Moon phases and Moonrise and Moonset times for your area by entering your zip code on the "Time and Date Moonrise and Moonset Calculator—City Lookup" web page (see the "Websites" section for the link).

explore

Moon Calendar

Note: If you would prefer to use the current month for your Moon calendar instead of the Moon calendar provided in this lesson, you can find calendars on several different websites. Our favorite is the McDonald Observatory site (see the "Websites" section).

> **SEP: Analyzing and Interpreting Data**
> Use observations (firsthand or from media) to describe patterns in the natural world in order to answer scientific questions.

Project the Moon Calendar student page and give each student a copy. Without giving any explanations of the page, tell students that you would like them to take a close look at the page and discuss what they notice. Encourage them to mark up the page with things they notice by circling, labeling, or highlighting. Model this on the projected calendar by using a marker to circle things, draw arrows and label, etc. (See example.)

T-Chart

Create a T-chart on the board or chart paper labeled "What Do You Notice? What Do You Wonder?" After students have had time to observe the calendar and talk with each other, ask them to share what they have noticed. Record these observations in the "What Do You Notice?" column of the T-chart.

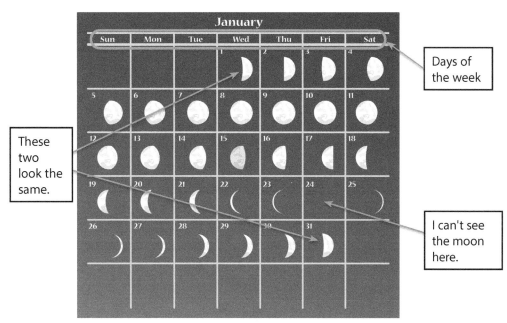

ANALYZING A MOON CALENDAR

Ask

? How would you describe the different shapes of the Moon on the calendar? (Point out the different shapes and have students describe them in their own words: e.g., banana-shaped, half circle.)

Questioning

> **SEP: Asking Questions and Defining Problems**
> Ask questions based on observations to find more information about the natural and/or designed worlds.

Next, ask students what they are wondering about the images on this sheet. Give them time to discuss with students nearby and then ask them to share. If students have trouble coming up with questions, you can model questions, such as the following:

? Why does the Moon look different in each box?

? What would come next after the last day of the calendar?

? Is there a pattern? Does it always happen in this order?

Record students' wonderings in the "What Do You Wonder?" column of the T-chart. Then ask

? How could we find the answers to these questions? (observe the Moon, read a nonfiction book, use internet resources, etc.)

explain

Next Time You See the Moon Read-Aloud

> Connecting to the Common Core
> **Reading: Informational Text**
> INTEGRATION OF KNOWLEDGE AND IDEAS: 1.7

AUTHOR EMILY MORGAN READING ALOUD

Making Connections: Text to World

Show students the cover of Next Time You See the Moon. Have the Moon calendar and T-chart nearby so that you can make connections to them as you read.

> **CCC: Patterns**
> Patterns in the natural world can be observed, used to describe phenomena, and used as evidence.

Read the book aloud. Here are examples of some connections to point out as you read:

- Page 7: "Have you ever recognized a pattern to the Moon's changing appearance?" Point to the calendar and ask students if anyone noticed a pattern.

- Page 8: "Have you ever wondered why the Moon appears to have different shapes at different times of the month?" This question will likely be on your T-chart.

- Page 21: "So when you look at the Moon today, know that you will see that same phase again about a month from now."

Point out on the Moon calendar that the phases of the Moon at the beginning of the month are the same at the end of the month.

- Pages 24–25: "In fact, scientists know what the Moon phase will be on any given date—even thousands of years into the future!"

Read the title of the graphic "A Year of Moon Phases." Point out the months listed along the left-hand side of the chart. Flip back to pages 22 and 23 and call attention to the order of the phases. Then turn back to pages 24 and 25 to point out how Moon phases follow this pattern throughout a year.

> **SEP: Obtaining, Evaluating, and Communicating Information**
> Read grade-appropriate texts and/or use media to obtain scientific and/or technical information to determine patterns in and/or evidence about the natural and designed world(s).

Take a look at the "What Do You Wonder?" column of the T-chart and discuss the questions that have been answered and the questions that still remain. Discuss the answers and add any new questions. You will likely have a question about why the Moon looks like it follows you. You can read the section titled "Fact or Fiction—Getting the Answers" on page 30 of A Moon of My Own that explains that objects that are far away seem to stay in the same place even when you move.

elaborate

Moon Wheel

Tell students that they can make a tool to help them remember the pattern of the Moon phases. Give each student a brass brad and the two Moon Wheel student pages copied on cardstock. Have students cut out each circle and the window on the smaller circle. They can use the brad to poke holes in the center of each circle and to connect the top circle to the bottom circle.

What Comes Next?

Note: If you decide to use the current month's Moon calendar, you can find the next month on

MAKING A MOON WHEEL

StarDate's Moon Phase Calculator web page (see the "Websites" section) by entering the month and year.

Revisit the Moon calendar student page. Note that the calendar ends on Friday, January 31. Ask

? What is the Moon phase on the last day of the month: Friday, January 31? (crescent)

? What day would come next on the calendar? (Saturday, February 1)

? What do you predict the Moon will look like on Saturday, February 1? (You may want to ask them to draw their answer.)

? What would be the next phase in the cycle? (Encourage students to use their Moon Wheels to predict the next phase. Students will likely predict a quarter Moon.)

> **CCC: Stability and Change**
> Some things stay the same while other things change.
> Things may change slowly or rapidly.

Project a copy of the February Moon Calendar page so that students can check their predictions. This is a good time to discuss that the eight named Moon phases on the Moon Wheel do not occur over eight consecutive days. The phases change much more slowly. For example, a crescent Moon will appear thicker each day as it approaches the quarter Moon phases. We can still refer to it as a crescent Moon during that transition. Remind students that the size and shape of the Moon do not change; the Moon is always the same sized sphere (ball). It is the lighted part we see that changes, giving us the different shapes that we call phases.

You may want to share the following rhyme to remind students if the Moon is waxing (we will see more of it in the coming days) or waning (we will see less of it in the coming days). "If the light is on the right, the Moon is getting bright." So, if the Moon is illuminated on the right-hand side, this means that we will see more of the Moon in the coming days. This rhyme only works if you are in the Northern Hemisphere though. In the Southern Hemisphere, the light would be on the opposite side!

evaluate

A Moon of My Own Silhouette Paintings

Revisit the book A Moon of My Own and ask students to notice the Moon phases. They can use their Moon Wheels to name the phases as you flip through the pages of the book.

Ask

? What do you notice about the Moon phases in the book? (They follow the pattern that the Moon actually follows.)

? Which Moon phase is missing from the book? (new Moon)

? Where in the story would the new Moon have occurred? (Between pages 11 and 12, before the page that reads "Each night you seem a little different from the night before.")

? Why do you think the illustrator left that Moon phase out of the book? (Because you can't see the Moon during new Moon.)

? What do you notice about the illustrations? (The Moon looks like it is glowing, the characters and settings are black on a blue background, and so on.)

? How do you think these illustrations were created? (Answers will vary.)

Read the section on page 31 titled "Moon Art" that explains how the illustrator, Ashley White, created her illustrations in silhouette. Tell students that they are going to have a chance to create a silhouette of themselves with the Moon phase of their choice. Point out how the illustrator made the Moon seem to glow in her illustrations. Have students look closely to see if they can figure out how. (The artist used lighter colors of blue around the Moon to make it seem to glow.) Tell students that first they will create the background of their silhouette. Give each student a piece of black construction paper and have them follow these instructions:

MOON SILHOUETTE PAINTING

1. With a pencil, sketch the Moon phase you choose in the center of your paper.
2. Fill in the Moon phase with white paint.
3. Outline your Moon with the lightest blue paint.
4. Outline that line with the second lightest paint.
5. Keep outlining the previous outline using the paints from lightest to darkest.

While the paint is drying, students can create silhouettes of themselves, trees, birds, bats, and so forth by drawing outlines on black construction paper and cutting them out.

When the paint is dry, students can glue their silhouettes on to the painted paper.

Moon Patterns

Give each student a copy of the Moon Patterns student page. Have them record the name of the phase they chose for their picture and the name of the next phase.

STEM Everywhere

Give students the STEM Everywhere student page as a way to involve their families and extend their learning. They can do the activity with an adult helper and share their results with the class. If students do not have access to the internet at home, you may choose to have them complete this activity at school.

Opportunities for Differentiated Instruction

This box lists questions and challenges related to the lesson that students may select to research, investigate, or innovate. Students may also use the questions as examples to help them generate their own questions. These questions can help you move your students from the teacher-directed investigation to engaging in the science and engineering practices in a more student-directed format.

Extra Support

For students who are struggling to meet the lesson objectives, provide a question and guide them in the process of collecting research or helping them design procedures or solutions.

Extensions

For students with high interest or who have already met the lesson objectives, have them choose a question (or pose their own question), conduct their own research, and design their own procedures or solutions.

After selecting one of the questions in this box or formulating their own questions, students can individually or collaboratively make predictions, design investigations or surveys to test their predictions, collect evidence, devise explanations, design solutions, or examine related resources. They can communicate their findings through a science notebook, at a poster session or gallery walk, or by producing a media project.

Research

Have students brainstorm researchable questions:

? What is a blue Moon and how often does it happen?

? What is a lunar eclipse and how often does it happen?

Continued

Opportunities for Differentiated Instruction (*continued*)

? What is a solar eclipse and how often does it happen?

Investigate

Have students brainstorm testable questions to be solved through science or math:

? What times are Moonrise and Moonset? Do the times change?

? Can you see the Moon during the day every day?

? Can you use the Moon wheel to predict the next phase you will see?

Innovate

Have students brainstorm problems to be solved through engineering:

? How can I make a model to represent the Moon phases?

? How can I create my own Moon calendar using my observations?

? What is the best way to photograph the Moon?

Websites

 StarDate's Moon Phase Calculator
https://stardate.org/nightsky/moon

 Story Time From Space: *A Moon of My Own*
https://storytimefromspace.com/a-moon-of-my-own-2

 Time and Date Moonrise and Moonset Calculator—City Lookup
www.timeanddate.com/moon

More Books to Read

DeCristofano, C. C. 2016. *The Sun and the Moon*. New York: Harper.
Summary: This Let's-Read-and-Find-Out Science book explains cycles of the Sun and the Moon, including the Moon phases and day/night. Simple text and vivid illustrations describe the features of the Sun and Moon as well. Includes a glossary and activities.

Olson, G. M. 2007. *Phases of the Moon*. Mankato, MN: Capstone Press.
Summary: From the Patterns in Nature series, this book uses simple text and photographs to show and describe the pattern of the Moon phases.

Name: _____

January Moon Calendar

What do you notice?

Look closely at the image below. Make notes about what you notice.
You can draw and write on the image.

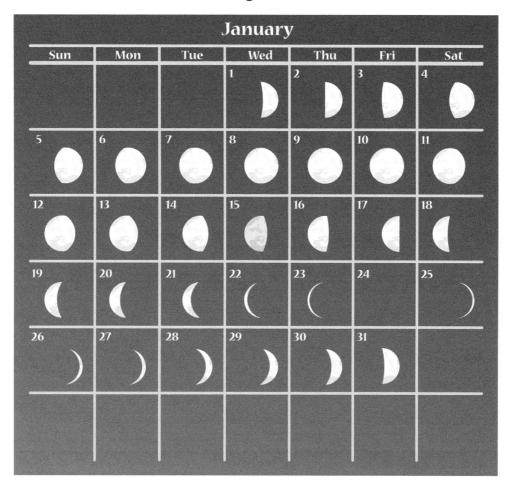

What do you wonder?

Write your questions here:

_____

_____

_____

February
Moon Calendar

February

Sun	Mon	Tue	Wed	Thu	Fri	Sat
						1
2	3	4	5	6	7	8
9	10	11	12	13	14	15
16	17	18	19	20	21	22
23	24	25	26	27	28	29

National Science Teaching Association

Moon Wheel 1

Instructions

1. Cut out the circle.
2. Cut out the window.
3. Use a brad to poke a hole in the center.

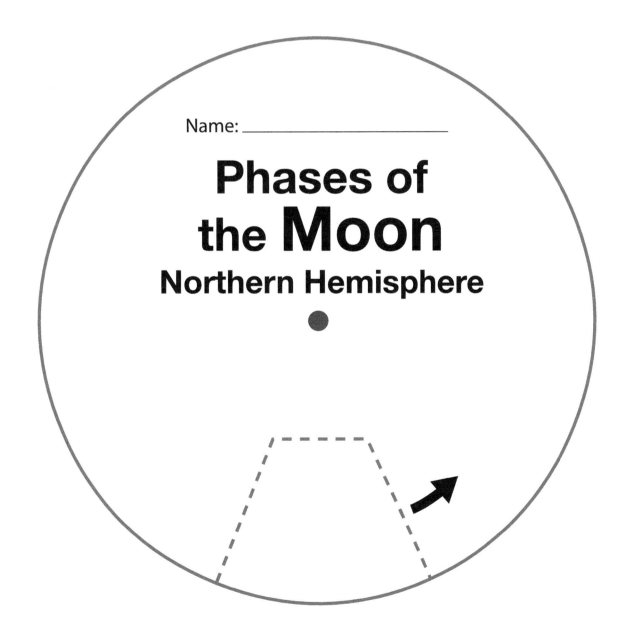

Name: _____

Phases of the **Moon**
Northern Hemisphere

Moon Wheel 2

Instructions
1. Cut out the circle.
2. Use a brad to poke a hole in the center.
3. Place the smaller circle on top.
4. Connect the two circles with a brad.

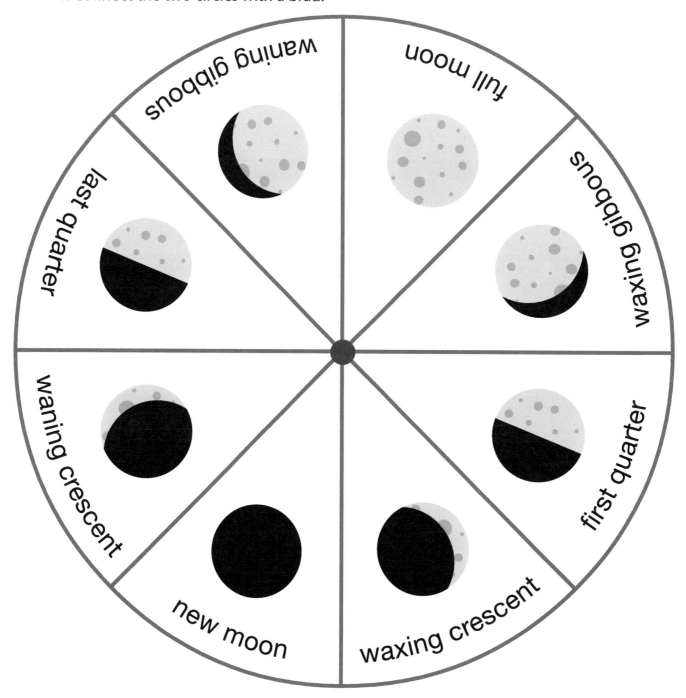

National Science Teaching Association

Name: _____

Moon Patterns

The Moon phases follow a pattern.

My painting shows a _____ Moon.

The next phase will be a _____ Moon.

Name: _____

Moon Patterns

The Moon phases follow a pattern.

My painting shows a _____ Moon.

The next phase will be a _____ Moon.

Name: _____

STEM Everywhere

Dear Families,

At school, we have been learning about how **the Moon phases occur in a predictable pattern.** We studied Moon calendars to identify the pattern and created a Moon Wheel to learn the phases and predict what comes next. To find out more, ask your learner the following questions and discuss their answers:

- What did you learn?

- What was your favorite part of the lesson?

- What are you still wondering?

 At home, you can visit a website to look at the Moon phases in the past and the future. Scan the QR code or go to *https://stardate.org/ nightsky/moon* and enter the month and year your learner was born. Click and you will see the Moon phases for that month. Find the day of the month, then draw the Moon phase on that date in the chart below. Repeat for your learner's next birthday. Next, find the Moon phases for two more important dates in your family's life. Remember, you can choose dates in the past AND the future. That's how predictable the Moon phases are!

Event	Date	Moon Phase Drawing
Birth date		
Next birthday		

National Science Teaching Association